the GI cookbook

lose weight the healthy way

using the glycaemic index

the  cookbook

lose weight the healthy way

using the glycaemic index

Gina Steer, Sian Lewis and Charlotte Watts

This is a Parragon Book
First published in 2005

Parragon
Queen Street House
4 Queen Street
Bath BA1 1HE, UK

ISBN: 1-40545-835-6

Printed in China

Produced by the Bridgewater Book Company Ltd.

Recipe photography: Clive Bozzard-Hill
Home economist: Sue Henderson

The Bridgewater Book Company would like to thank The
Ivy Press Limited for permission to reproduce copyright
material on pages 11 (nuts), 12, 13 and 15.

NOTE

This book uses metric and imperial measurements.
Follow the same units of measurement throughout; do
not mix metric and imperial. All spoon measurements
are level: teaspoons are assumed to be 5 ml, and
tablespoons are assumed to be 15 ml. Unless
otherwise stated, milk is assumed to be full fat, eggs
and individual vegetables such as potatoes are
medium, and pepper is freshly ground black pepper.

The times given for each recipe are an approximate
guide only. Preparation times differ according to the
techniques used by different people, and the cooking
times may vary as a result of the types of oven and
other equipment used.

Recipes using raw or very lightly cooked eggs should
be avoided by infants, the elderly, pregnant women,
convalescents and anyone suffering from an illness.
Pregnant and breast-feeding women are advised
to avoid eating peanuts and peanut products.

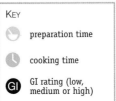

KEY

preparation time

cooking time

GI GI rating (low,
medium or high)

Contents

Introduction

The GI diet is an exciting new way of eating for a healthier lifestyle, offering a solution to the common problem of losing weight while still following a well-balanced diet.

We are all increasingly aware of good nutrition and its connection with health. With clinical obesity on the increase, both in adults and, more worryingly, in children, it is no surprise that diet-related cookbooks have become incredibly popular. While some of these books concentrate primarily on the problems of excess weight, this book goes further by viewing the issue of losing weight within the wider context of an overall healthy lifestyle. Furthermore, unlike some diets, it avoids setting idealistic goals that can be difficult to follow, recommending a diet that is either expensive or unrealistic, or one that cuts out some everyday foods. Finally, with so-called 'magic' or 'crash' diets, the weight quickly piles back on once these foods are re-introduced when the diet is over – the GI diet avoids the crash and, by changing the way you balance your foods for life, it may never really end as other diets do.

Nutrition is an issue for us all and the link between a healthy life and what we eat has long been recognized by both doctors and nutritionists alike. Eating correctly reduces the risk of heart disease, stroke, diabetes, obesity, some food allergies, and can help in the fight against cancer. However, there are many conflicting messages in the media regarding the link between diet and good health, and it is easy to get confused. The fast-food culture is now an integral part of life, and it is all too easy to opt for a take-away, as time is short. This book helps to provide the answer, offering quick, simple recipes that are ideal when pursuing a healthy diet and lifestyle.

The first chapter of this book reveals the mysteries of the GI (Glycaemic Index) table, highlighting foods that should be eaten on a daily basis in order to meet the energy demands we need, plus explaining why it is important not to cut out fat altogether from your diet but to choose sensible amounts of the right types – a quality, not quantity issue.

This chapter is followed by more than 40 practical recipes, all nutritionally analysed, which will help you to achieve and maintain a healthy lifestyle. The recipes are delicious, suitable for all the family and easy to prepare and cook. There are dishes that will satisfy the heartiest of appetites as well as stimulating a jaded palate. The food in this book is tempting and appealing, a far cry from the tired, limp salads, sad-looking vegetables and brown-coloured meals which many people associate with healthy food.

A good diet, however, is not alone in the pursuit of a healthy lifestyle: exercise also plays an important part, so try to make time for this. You'll find additional information on exercise and eating out. Exercise is not the preserve of the fit – everyone can do it, so don't be put off. If you are starting from scratch, the secret is to do it gradually.

So be kind to yourself and your family and serve them food that not only will keep them fit and healthy – but that they will also love. Eat your way to good health!

1

nutrition and lifestyle

The Glycaemic Index and a healthy diet

The Glycaemic Index

The Glycaemic Index (GI) is a system whereby ingredients and dishes are rated according to the rate at which a carbohydrate food breaks down into simple sugars and enters the bloodstream – we should be aiming for a slow, steady release for good blood sugar balance (see page 14). A low-GI diet can be extremely useful not only for people wanting to control their blood sugar levels but also for those wanting to lose weight, reduce the risk of heart disease and boost their energy levels.

A GI diet is not only extremely healthy, it can also be great for losing weight.

What are the benefits of a low-GI diet?

• Low GI means a smaller rise in blood sugar levels after meals.
• Low GI foods tend to contain more fibre so keep you feeling fuller for longer.
• Low GI can help you lose weight as it promotes the use of fat over carbohydrate and protein for fuel by the body.
• Low GI can improve blood sugar control.
• Low GI can prolong physical endurance.
• Low GI can make you feel less tired and lethargic.

It is important to note that a low-GI diet, like any diet, needs to be balanced. No single food contains all the nutrients that you need as different foods are rich in a range of nutrients. In order to achieve a healthy, balanced diet you need to eat a variety of different foods every day, paying particular attention to both the quantity and the type of food chosen.

How can you achieve a healthy diet?

• Eat a variety of different foods from each food group.
• Eat regularly, never miss a meal.
• Choose high-fibre, wholemeal products.
• Eat more fruit and vegetables, at least five portions a day.
• Choose healthy sources of fats such as avocados, olive oil, raw nuts and seeds, oily fish and some lean white meat, rather than red meat and dairy products.
• Choose lean meat, fish, poultry, beans and vegetarian alternatives instead of fatty meats or meat products.
• Eat oily fish two to three times a week.

If you follow these general guidelines your body will be getting all the essential nutrients – carbohydrates, fat, protein, fibre, vitamins and minerals – that it needs on a daily basis.

What affects GI value?

• Cooking – when you heat starchy foods up they will be digested more easily.
• Processing – processed foods are more refined so make the starches they contain faster to digest.
• Fat and protein – foods high in protein and fat are emptied more slowly from your stomach. They take longer to digest and so slow the breakdown and sugar release from carbohydrate foods
• Acid – by adding an acidic food to your meal the GI value will be lowered so it takes longer for your stomach to digest, eg, dressing added to a salad.

How can you achieve a low-GI diet?

Including a low-GI food with each meal or snack will lower the overall effect of your blood sugar levels and make them more stable. By doing so you will feel less hungry in between meals and have more energy. You need to choose fewer processed foods and more high-fibre foods.

Achieving a low-GI diet

Breakfast

• Choose oat-based breakfast cereals.

• Add fruit and raw nuts to cereals.

• Have fresh fruit rather than juice.

• Eat 'grainy' breads made with whole seeds.

Lunch

• Eat plenty of salads.

• Choose chunky bean or vegetable soups.

• Add variety with different types of breads, eg, pumpernickel, multi-grain.

Evening meal

• Use brown basmati rice, bulgar wheat or pearl barley.

• Include plenty of beans and lentils.

• Eat plenty of vegetables.

• Reduce the amount of potatoes you eat.

Desserts

• Try more fruit-based desserts.

• Add nuts to puddings

Glycaemic Index ratings for some common foods

The Glycaemic Index rates carbohydrate foods from 0 to 100 and measures the rise in blood sugar levels caused by a particular food, whether it be a dramatic rise, moderate or low. Carbohydrate foods are those that contain glucose, which is found in plant foods. Cheese, eggs, fish and meat contain only fat and protein and so cannot be included in the table.

The rating is determined by giving enough of a particular food to provide 50 g of carbohydrate and then measuring what effect this has on blood sugar levels. All foods are compared to the effect pure glucose has on blood glucose – which is given as an arbitrary figure of 100. You should aim for a range of low-GI foods in your diet.

Foods are given a score out of 100 and are classified as follows:

Foods that are quickly absorbed	GI	more than 70
Foods that take a moderate amount of time to be absorbed	GI	value 55–70
Foods that take longer to be absorbed	GI	less than 55

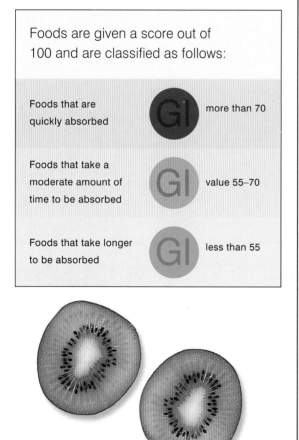

GI Low Foods

Fruit and Fruit Juices

Tomatoes	(15)
Cherries	(22)
Grapefruit	(25)
Dried apricots	(31)
Pears	(37)
Apples	(38)
Plums	(39)
Strawberries	(40)
Apple juice	(41)
Peaches	(42)
Oranges	(44)
Grapes	(46)
Pineapple juice	(46)
Grapefruit juice	(48)
Orange juice	(52)
Kiwi fruit	(53)
Bananas	(54)

Vegetables

Broccoli	(10)
Cabbage	(10)
Lettuce	(10)
Mushrooms	(10)
Raw onions	(10)
Raw red peppers	(10)
Green peas	(48)
Raw carrots	(49)
Sweet potatoes	(54)

Grains

Pearl barley	(31)
Rye	(34)
Brown basmati rice	(52)

Breads

Mixed-grain bread	(48)
German rye bread	(50)

Pasta

Vermicelli	(35)
Linguine	(42)
Instant noodles	(47)

Bakery Products

Sponge cake (with egg)	(46)

Breakfast Cereals

Bran cereal	(42)

Dairy

Low-fat natural yogurt	(14)
Full-fat milk	(27)
Skimmed milk	(27)
Low-fat fruit yogurt	(33)
Custard	(43)

Legumes

Soya beans	(14)
Red split lentils	(18)
Green lentils	(29)
Canned chickpeas	(42)
Canned pinto beans	(45)
Canned baked beans	(48)
Green peas	(48)

GI Medium Foods

Fruit

Mangoes	(56)
Sultanas	(56)
Apricots	(57)
Raisins	(64)
Pineapple	(66)

Vegetables

Sweetcorn	(55)
New potatoes	(57)
Beetroot	(64)
Boiled/mashed potatoes	(70)

Grains

Brown rice	(55)
Buckwheat	(55)
White basmati rice	(58)

Breads

White pitta bread	(58)
Hamburger buns	(61)
Rye flour bread	(64)
High-fibre wheat bread	(68)
Wholemeal wheat bread	(69)

Pasta

Durum wheat spaghetti	(55)

Bakery Products

Pastry	(59)
Muffins	(62)
Croissants	(67)
Crumpets	(69)

Breakfast Cereals

Muesli	(56)
Porridge	(61)
Wholewheat shredded biscuits	(69)
Wheat biscuits	(70)

Biscuits

Oatmeal	(55)
Rich tea	(55)
Digestives	(59)
Shortbread	(64)

Savoury Biscuits and Crackers

Wheat thins	(67)

Dairy

Ice cream	(61)

Sugars

High-fruit jam	(55)
Honey	(58)
White granulated sugar	(64)

Sweets and Snacks

Popcorn	(55)

Beverages

Orange cordial	(66)
Fizzy orange	(68)

GI High Foods

Fruit

Watermelon	(72)

Vegetables

Swede	(72)
Chips	(75)
Pumpkin	(75)
Baked potato	(85)
Cooked carrots	(85)
Parsnips	(97)

Grains

White rice	(88)

Breads

White bagels	(72)
White wheat bread	(78)
Gluten-free bread	(90)
French baguette	(95)

Bakery Products

Doughnuts	(76)
Waffles	(76)

Breakfast Cereals

Bran flakes with dried fruit	(71)
Puffed wheat	(74)
Crisped rice	(82)
Corn flakes	(83)

Savoury Biscuits and Crackers

Water biscuits	(71)
Rice cakes	(77)
Puffed crispbread	(81)

Legumes

Broad beans	(79)

Sweets and Snacks

Corn tortillas	(74)
Jelly beans	(80)
Pretzels	(81)
Dates	(99)

Beverages

High-glucose sports drinks	(95)

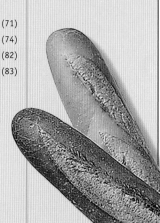

Carbohydrates

Carbohydrates are plant foods (except lactose in milk) and found in a variety of sources. Their primary role is to provide your body with energy so about 50 per cent of your total daily calories should come from carbohydrates. Carbohydrates are broken down by your digestive system into glucose and transported along your bloodstream to parts of the body needing energy – such as your muscles and brain.

Carbohydrates are either 'simple' (sugars) or 'complex' (starches). You should limit your intake of sugars and get most of your energy requirements from starches.

Simple carbohydrates or sugars are found in processed foods, sweets, cakes, soft drinks, fruit juices and very refined carbohydrates, such as white bread, where the bran part of the wheat has been stripped away.

Complex carbohydrates release their sugars more slowly and are termed *starches*. They also contain *fibre* that helps to slow down sugar release and take toxins out of the body to help prevent disease. Vegetables, nuts, pulses, wholegrains and fruits in their raw, natural state provide complex carbohydrates bound in fibre. They therefore take much more time to breakdown into their simple sugars and provide a more slow and steady release into the bloodstream.

The importance of exercise

Regular exercise is an essential part of a healthy lifestyle. If you want to reduce your risk of developing disease, increase your life expectancy and improve your quality of life when you are old, then you need to stay active. Half the battle with exercise is motivating yourself to start and then keeping it up on a regular basis, but there are plenty of good reasons to keep you going. Both your body and your mind will reap tremendous benefits from physical activity.

The physical benefits of exercise

Exercise protects your physical health and has many positive effects on how your body works – your heart muscles become stronger and pump more blood more quickly around your body to pick up fatty deposits and waste products. As a result, blood pressure and cholesterol levels are lowered, reducing your risk of developing heart disease or stroke. Your lungs become stronger and your body more efficient in the way in which it uses oxygen. Bones stay strong and healthy, muscles become stronger and joint mobility and stability will improve, helping to keep you independent and active in later life. As you age, your metabolism (the rate at which your body uses energy) slows down and your body needs fewer calories, but if you remain active you will avoid excess weight gain in old age because physical activity boosts your metabolic rate.

How exercise benefits your mind

Regular exercise can improve your psychological well-being. When you exercise, your brain releases morphine-like chemicals called endorphins that act as natural anti-depressants to make you feel relaxed and in a good mood. The feeling of well-being that follows exercise will reduce any stress and tension. By exercising regularly you are more likely to feel and look healthy, which will increase your confidence and self-esteem.

The other nutrients

Fats

Fat has had a bad press. We need fat in the diet for resistance to infection, hormone function, cholesterol regulation, healthy cell membranes and optimum mental function. It is important to adopt a healthy attitude to fats and realize that they are not all bad and that we are made up of a large proportion of fat – they make up more than 60 per cent of your brain and need to be continually replenished for good mental function, concentration, memory and mood.

Fats are crucial in your diet to ensure that you obtain all the nutrients you need on a daily basis. They provide essential fatty acids and are carriers for certain vitamins. You do not have to cut out fats completely in your diet to lose weight – what is important is to look at how much fat you eat. Fat provides energy – 1 gram provides 9 kcals so if a food contains a lot of fat it means that it also provides you with a lot of calories. For example, an average serving of butter on toast contains 9 grams of fat which provides 81 kcals, so if you swapped this for a low-fat margarine you would have 3.6 grams of fat and 32 kcals.

Fats are made up of fatty acids and glycerol and are divided into saturated or unsaturated. It is recommended that no more than 35 per cent of your total daily calories should come from fats, 10 per cent being from saturated fats. This means that if your calorie intake was 2000 kcals per day only 35 per cent should be from fats. As each gram of fat provides 9 kcals, your total daily intake of should be no more than 77.8 g fat – that's just over 3 oz.

SATURATED FATS are the fats that you should reduce in your diet as high intakes can lead to an increase in your blood cholesterol levels, which in turn increases the risk of coronary heart disease. Main sources in your diet are dairy foods including butter, cheese, cream, milk, fatty meats and lard. As a rule of thumb, saturated fats tend to be a solid at room

A balance of unsaturated fats is essential for a healthy diet.

temperature and are derived from animal sources. However, there are exceptions – coconut and palm oil, plus some margarines and oils labelled 'hydrogenated'. The latter should be avoided in your diet as during processing some of their unsaturated fats are changed to saturated fats.

UNSATURATED FATS can be divided into two types – polyunsaturated and monounsaturated. There are two types of polyunsaturated fats, Omega 3 and Omega 6. Omega 3 are from oily, coldwater fish such as mackerel, herring, salmon, tuna, trout, sardines and anchovies. However, these can contain high levels of mercury or other toxins, so it is best to limit your intake to about three times a week. The smaller the fish, the less mercury it will have accumulated. The best vegetarian sources are flax (linseed), hemp and pumpkin seeds and their cold-pressed oils.

Omega 6 are of vegetable or plant origin, including hemp seed, Evening Primrose Oil, borage, sunflower seeds, pumpkin seeds and sesame seeds and their oils. Nuts, except peanuts, are also good sources. Polyunsaturated fats tend to be liquid at room temperature and it is essential to include them in your diet as they can help to reduce blood cholesterol levels and maintain good health.

Monounsaturated fats are considered to protect against heart disease as they can help to reduce your blood cholesterol levels. They can be found in foods like olive oil, rapeseed oil, avocados, peanuts, almonds and oily fish.

Protein

Protein is found in meat, fish, eggs and dairy products as well as beans, peas, lentils and other vegetarian alternatives. Its main purpose is to provide building blocks for growth and maintenance of your muscles and tissues so 10–15 per cent of your total daily calories should come from protein. If your diet is varied and balanced, containing some protein at each meal, you should be able to meet your daily protein requirements. Overly high intakes can lead to health problems such as kidney diseases.

Protein is made up of amino acids – there are 20 naturally occurring and protein foods contain varying amounts of each. Your body is also able to make up some amino acids from your diet but there are eight that it cannot make. These are known as essential amino acids and must be obtained from your diet.

Once eaten, protein is broken down into amino acids and absorbed in the small intestine. The acids are then transported to the liver for processing and released into your bloodstream to make up enzymes, hormones, body cells, hair, nails, bones, muscles and DNA. Your body is always recombining amino acids to make new cells and nearly all your body cells are able to make specific protein for their needs.

Fibre

Fibre is a form of carbohydrate the we do not use for fuel. Also called non-starch polysaccharide, it is simply the skeleton part of plants. It is found mainly in the outer walls of plants and seeds.

Fibre passes through your digestive system rather than being digested and absorbed into the body. You should aim for 18 g of fibre a day so it is important that you include a variety of high-fibre foods each day in your diet. There are two types of fibre in your diet, each with a different role:

Insoluble fibre is found in wheat bran, whole-grain bread and cereals, and fruit and vegetables. It helps maintain a healthy digestive system as it holds water and increases bulk, which stimulates the muscles of your digestive system. This means that the muscles in your digestive system are kept healthy and toned, helping to prevent constipation, haemorrhoids and bowel cancer.

Soluble fibre, found in oats, beans, dried or canned pulses, and fruit and vegetables, plays a role in lowering blood cholesterol.

Be warned – if you increase your fibre intake to ensure a healthy, balanced diet you must also drink plenty of fluids, at least 8–10 glasses a day.

Cheese, a source of protein, can be beneficial for a balanced diet.

Eating a range of fruits can supply soluble and insoluble fibre.

Vitamins and minerals

Most people are able to meet their daily requirements for vitamins and minerals by eating a varied diet. At times some people may have higher requirements, eg during illness, later life, when pregnant or on certain medication, and they will need to ensure that they eat foods rich in certain vitamins and minerals. They could also be advised to take supplements to compensate.

Vitamins are needed to carry out many processes in your body and are grouped into two categories; fat soluble (vitamins A, D, E and K) and water soluble (vitamins C, B_1, B_2, B_5, B_6, B_{12}, niacin, biotin and folic acid). Vitamins are susceptible to damage by heat, light, oxygen, enzymes and minerals, and losses can occur during food processing, preparation and storage. All nutrients work together in synergy for body functions.

Water contains vital minerals.

Minerals are needed in larger amounts than vitamins, for a variety of functions in your body. Absorption of minerals can be influenced by a variety of factors:
- Iron absorption is increased when vitamin C is eaten at the same meal.
- Zinc absorption is reduced when there is an excess intake of iron.
- Iodine absorption is reduced by nitrates.
- Phytates and oxalates hinder the absorption of calcium, iron and zinc.

Eating out and entertaining

For most people, the hardest part of weight control is not dieting but keeping the weight off permanently. Long-term weight management doesn't mean you can't entertain, go out, or take part in the Christmas festivities. Here are some ideas to help you keep in control of what's on your plate.

Anticipate If you know you're entertaining or going out to dinner, try eating very healthily the day before and plan to fit in some exercise to compensate, even if it's just a long walk the day after. It also helps to think about what you might order before you go out so that you can choose the healthiest options on the menu and not be tempted to try everything on the cheeseboard.

Keep it plain Choose food that is cooked simply and not drowned in high-calorie sauces – grilled fish and meat are good options.

Say no to the extras Stick to what you've ordered and avoid the extra calories lurking in the bread and olive oil, the poppadoms and chutneys, the nachos and cheese.

Skip the starter or dessert Limit yourself to two courses and save calories.

Buffet management When serving yourself at a buffet, try limiting yourself to two or three types of food on your plate at a time. Start with the low-calorie options – the vegetables and salads – to leave less room for more fattening foods.

How to deal with alcohol Alcohol is an appetite stimulant and because it relaxes your inhibitions you are more likely to be careless over what you eat. Never drink on an empty stomach – if you know you're going out drinking, eat something light beforehand. Always start off with a soft drink or water, and match every alcoholic drink with a non-alcoholic one.

2

breakfasts and brunches

Midsummer Smoothie

5 minutes

no cooking required

GI low

Smoothies provide a quick, healthy and delicious drink that's both filling and nutritious – ideal when there is no time to sit and eat or as a refreshing early morning starter.

SERVES 2

115 g/4 oz strawberries

115 g/4 oz raspberries

55 g/2 oz blueberries

1 ripe passion fruit

150 ml/5 fl oz semi-skimmed milk

TO DECORATE

2 scoops frozen strawberry yogurt or 1 tbsp crushed ice and 2 tbsp Greek yogurt

2 strawberries

1 Lightly rinse the strawberries, raspberries and blueberries, and scoop out the passion fruit pulp. Place all the fruits in a juicer or liquidizer and blend for 1 minute. Add the milk and blend again.

2 Either pour into tall glasses and top with the yogurt or place some crushed ice in glasses, pour in the fruit juice and place the scoops of yogurt on top. Decorate with strawberries.

Serving Analysis			
Energy (kcals)	68	Protein (grams)	4.3
Total fat (grams)	1.5	Carbohydrate (grams)	11.6
of which saturated fat (grams)	0.2	of which sugars (grams)	11.6
Fat/100 g product (grams)	**0.5**		

10 minutes

10–12 minutes

GI low

Toasted Muesli

This delicious crunchy muesli can be eaten on its own with a little skimmed or semi-skimmed milk or sprinkled over grapefruit segments or melon chunks with strawberries.

SERVES 4

225 g/8 oz jumbo porridge oats

85 g/3 oz dried apricots, roughly chopped

55 g/2 oz raisins

25 g/1 oz dried cranberries

25 g/1 oz wheat bran

TO SERVE

skimmed milk

fresh fruit, such as sliced banana, strawberries and blueberries

1 Preheat the oven to 200°C/400°F/Gas Mark 6. Pour the porridge oats into a shallow dish. Cook in the oven for 10–12 minutes, or until the oats are golden. Stir the oats occasionally. Remove and leave to cool then place in a bowl.

2 Add the apricots, raisins, cranberries and wheat bran and place in an airtight container. Serve 3–4 tablespoons of the muesli in bowls with skimmed milk and top with fresh fruit.

Serving Analysis			
Energy (kcals)	129	Protein (grams)	4.3
Total fat (grams)	2.3	Carbohydrate (grams)	23
of which saturated fat (grams)	0.4	of which sugars (grams)	5.1
Fat/100 g product (grams)	**0.05**		

12 minutes

23 minutes

GI low

Mushroom Cups

Large field mushrooms can be served with a variety of fillings, such as roasted vegetables, three-bean salad or stir-fried peppers and onion.

SERVES 4

2 red peppers, deseeded and cut into quarters

4–8 field mushrooms, depending on size

1–2 tsp extra virgin olive oil

85 g/3 oz French beans, trimmed

1 egg

2 egg whites

2 tbsp skimmed milk

1 tbsp chopped fresh flat-leaf parsley

salt and pepper

grilled tomatoes, to serve (optional)

1 Preheat the grill and line the grill rack with tin foil. Place the red pepper under the grill and cook for 5–8 minutes, or until the skins are charred. Turn the peppers occasionally so they are evenly charred. Transfer the peppers to a polythene bag and leave until cool. When cool enough to handle, remove the skin.

2 Wipe the mushrooms then remove and discard the stalks. Heat the oil in a frying pan and very gently sauté the mushrooms for 4–5 minutes, or until lightly cooked. (Cover the frying pan with a lid to help with the cooking process.)

3 Meanwhile, cook the French beans in lightly boiling water for 4 minutes, drain and keep warm.

4 To make the scrambled egg filling, beat the egg with the egg whites, milk and seasoning to taste. Stir in the parsley. Heat a small non-stick frying pan then pour in the egg mixture. Cook, stirring occasionally, over a medium heat for 4–5 minutes, or until lightly set.

5 Place 2 pepper quarters and beans on warmed serving plates then fill the mushroom cups with the scrambled egg mixture. Place on top of the beans. Serve with grilled tomatoes if liked.

Serving Analysis			
Energy (kcals)	58	Protein (grams)	4.9
Total fat (grams)	2.8	Carbohydrate (grams)	3.4
of which saturated fat (grams)	0.7	of which sugars (grams)	3
Fat/100 g product (grams)	2		

Date and Banana Muffins

15 minutes

10–20 minutes

GI medium

It is not a good idea to skip breakfast so if you are in a rush, take a muffin with you – it will keep you going through the morning, thus avoiding the need to nibble. For low-GI muffins, replace the dates with apricots.

SERVES 6–12 (nutritional information for 6)

225 g/8 oz self-raising wholemeal flour	55 g/2 oz chopped dates
1 tsp baking powder	1 ripe banana, peeled and mashed
1 tsp ground cinnamon	1 egg, beaten
25 g/1 oz wheat bran	2 egg whites
25 g/1 oz light muscovado sugar	up to 150 ml/5 fl oz orange juice

1 Preheat the oven to 180°C/350°F/Gas Mark 4. Place 6 paper muffin cases into a muffin tin or 12 paper baking cases into a bun tin. Sift the flour, baking powder and ground cinnamon into a mixing bowl then tip in the bran residue that is left in the sieve plus the 25 g/1 oz of bran.

2 Stir in the sugar, dates and mashed banana. Add the egg and egg whites, then mix in sufficient orange juice to give a soft dropping consistency. Spoon into the paper cases.

3 Bake in the oven for 10–20 minutes, or until risen and the tops spring back when touched lightly with a clean finger. Remove and serve warm.

Cook's Tip

Muffins are always best eaten warm so make these ahead of time and either reheat for 30–40 seconds in a microwave or in a conventional oven for about 5 minutes.

Serving Analysis			
Energy (kcals)	205	Protein (grams)	8.1
Total fat (grams)	2.2	Carbohydrate (grams)	41.1
of which saturated fat (grams)	0.5	of which sugars (grams)	16.4
Fat/100 g product (grams)	**1.9**		

Fruity Porridge

5 minutes

8–10 minutes

GI low

This recipe can be made the evening before and left refrigerated overnight, or made in the morning and eaten immediately. It is perfect to sustain the whole family throughout the morning.

SERVES 4

175 g/6 oz jumbo porridge oats

55 g/2 oz oatmeal

pinch of salt (optional)

850 ml/1½ pints skimmed milk

55 g/2 oz dried apricots, chopped

15 g/1 oz sunflower seeds

sliced banana, to serve

1 Place the oats and oatmeal in a saucepan together with the salt, if using, and stir in the milk. Place over a gentle heat and cook, stirring, for 7–8 minutes, or until the oats thicken.

2 Stir the apricots and sunflower seeds into the porridge, spoon into individual dishes and top with the sliced banana. Alternatively, place the porridge in the dishes and top with the fruits and seeds.

Cook's Tip

If you want to make the porridge the evening before, place the oats, oatmeal, salt and milk into the top of a double boiler and cook over gently simmering water for about 25–30 minutes, or until thickened. Remove from the heat. The following day reheat the porridge gently, stirring occasionally, and serve topped with the fruit and seeds.

Serving Analysis			
Energy (kcals)	164	Protein (grams)	7.8
Total fat (grams)	3.5	Carbohydrate (grams)	26.5
of which saturated fat (grams)	0.5	of which sugars (grams)	7.9
Fat/100 g product (grams)	2.4		

12 minutes

12 minutes

GI low

Smoked Salmon with Broccoli

This dish is an ideal choice for brunch, together with Date and Banana Muffins and a Midsummer Smoothie.

Cook's Tip

Place pastry cutters in the water and poach the eggs in them so they keep their shape.

SERVES 4

225 g/8 oz broccoli

4 eggs

2 tsp lemon juice (optional)

225 g/8 oz smoked salmon

wholemeal or Granary bread, to serve

DRESSING

150 ml/5 fl oz 8% fat fromage frais

1–1½ tsp Dijon mustard

2 tsp snipped fresh chives

1 Divide the broccoli into spears then cook in boiling water for 5–6 minutes, or until tender. Drain and keep warm while you poach the eggs.

2 To poach the eggs, half-fill a large frying pan with water, add the lemon juice, if using, and bring to the boil. Reduce the heat to a simmer then carefully break 1 egg into a cup then slip into the simmering water. Repeat with the remaining eggs. Poach the eggs for 4–5 minutes, or until set to personal preference.

3 Meanwhile, divide the smoked salmon between 4 individual plates. Stir all the dressing ingredients together in a mixing jug until blended.

4 Place the broccoli spears on the plates, top each with a poached egg, spoon over a little dressing and serve. Serve with wholemeal or Granary bread.

Serving Analysis			
Energy (kcals)	143	Protein (grams)	20.7
Total fat (grams)	3.6	Carbohydrate (grams)	7.4
of which saturated fat (grams)	0.8	of which sugars (grams)	7.2
Fat/100 g product (grams)	**1.2**		

Vegetable Rösti

20 minutes

12 minutes

GI low

Quick and easy to prepare and cook, Vegetable Rösti is ideal to serve both as a main component of breakfast or brunch or as an accompaniment to a main meal.

SERVES 4

1 carrot, grated

1 courgette, grated

1 sweet potato, grated

8 spring onions, finely chopped or shredded

1 egg white, beaten

2 tsp extra virgin olive oil

pepper

8 lean back bacon rashers, to serve (optional)

1 Mix all the vegetables together, season with pepper to taste then stir in the egg white. Using clean hands, form into 8 small patties. Press them firmly together.

2 Heat the oil in a non-stick frying pan and cook the patties over a gentle heat for 5–6 minutes, or until golden. Turn over halfway through the cooking time and press down with the back of a spatula. Do this in 2 batches to prevent the pan from being overcrowded.

3 Meanwhile, preheat the grill and line the grill rack with tin foil. Place the bacon under the grill and cook for 5-8 minutes, until crisp, or cook to personal preference. Turn the rashers over halfway through the cooking time.

4 As soon as the patties and bacon are cooked serve immediately.

Cook's Tip

If liked, cook as 1 large rösti. Place all the mixture in the heated frying pan and press down with a spatula. Cook for 6–8 minutes then invert onto a large plate and slip the mixture back into the frying pan. Cook for a further 4–6 minutes.

Serving Analysis

Energy (kcals)	280	Protein (grams)	26.3
Total fat (grams)	16.9	Carbohydrate (grams)	6.1
of which saturated fat (grams)	6.2	of which sugars (grams)	3.4
Fat/100 g product (grams)	9.9		

15 minutes

40 minutes

GI low

Saffron-flavoured Fish

You can vary the fish used here according to personal preference. Smoked or fresh salmon, trout or even prawns would work well.

SERVES 4

115 g/4 oz brown basmati rice

1 tsp extra virgin olive oil

1 onion, cut into small wedges

1–2 fresh red chillies, to taste, deseeded and chopped

few saffron strands

1/2–1 tsp ground coriander

700 ml/1 1/4 pints vegetable or fish stock

350 g/12 oz white fish fillet, such as cod or haddock

115 g/4 oz undyed smoked haddock

115 g/4 oz broccoli

225 g/8 oz cherry tomatoes, halved

4–6 spring onions, trimmed and chopped

pepper

1 tbsp chopped fresh coriander

1 Rinse the rice and shake off any excess water. Heat the oil in a large frying pan, add the rice, onion and chillies and cook over a medium heat, stirring, for 2 minutes. Add the saffron strands and ground coriander and cook for a further 1 minute before pouring in half of the stock. Bring to the boil then reduce the heat to a simmer and cover. Cook for 15 minutes, stirring occasionally and adding more stock as necessary so that the rice does not dry out.

2 Meanwhile, skin the fish and remove any pin bones, rinse, then cut into small pieces. Set aside. Divide the broccoli into tiny florets and cook in lightly boiling water for 5 minutes. Drain and keep warm. Add the fish to the rice and cook for a further 5 minutes.

3 Add the tomatoes and broccoli to the rice and fish mixture and cook for a further 5 minutes before adding the spring onions, pepper to taste and coriander. Cook for 2–3 minutes, or until the rice is tender but retains a bite. Serve immediately.

Serving Analysis			
Energy (kcals)	239	Protein (grams)	26.2
Total fat (grams)	2.8	Carbohydrate (grams)	27.1
of which saturated fat (grams)	0.3	of which sugars (grams)	3.5
Fat/100 g product (grams)	**1.1**		

light snacks and starters

Spicy Hummus

5 minutes

no cooking required

GI low

This dip can be served on many different occasions, as an appetizer, light lunch or even as an accompaniment to a main meal in place of rice, potato or pasta.

SERVES 6

400 g/14 oz canned chickpeas, drained and rinsed

2–4 garlic cloves, peeled and crushed

1 fresh red chilli, deseeded and chopped

2 tbsp tahini

4 tbsp lime juice

2–4 tbsp cooled boiled water

1 tbsp chopped fresh coriander

pepper

CRUDITES

2 carrots, peeled and cut into sticks

1 red pepper, deseeded and cut into strips

1/2 cucumber, peeled if preferred and cut into strips

4 celery sticks, trimmed and cut into small strips

Cook's tip

If using dried chickpeas, rinse thoroughly and soak overnight. The following day, drain, place in a saucepan and cover with water. Bring to the boil then discard the water. Cover with fresh water, bring to the boil then simmer for 1 hour, or until tender. Drain and proceed as above.

1 Place the chickpeas, garlic and chilli in a food processor and blend for 1 minute or until finely chopped. Add the tahini and blend again for 30 seconds.

2 With the motor still running, gradually pour in the lime juice and then sufficient water to give a soft dipping consistency.

3 Add pepper to taste and the chopped coriander and blend for a further 1 minute. Scrape into a small bowl and serve with Crudités.

Serving Analysis

Energy (kcals)	138	Protein (grams)	6.9
Total fat (grams)	5.2	Carbohydrate (grams)	16.8
of which saturated fat (grams)	0.7	of which sugars (grams)	5.3
Fat/100 g product (grams)	**2.7**		

10 mins, plus 30 minutes' soaking

no cooking required

GI low

Tomato and Olive Dip

This dip is ideal to serve with a salad instead of a dressing or mayonnaise or as an alternative sauce to accompany the Thai-style Fish Cakes.

SERVES 6

15 g/¹/₂ oz sun-dried tomatoes

25 g/1 oz black olives, stoned

1 tsp tomato purée

250 g/9 oz Quark

2 tbsp orange or lemon juice

pinch of paprika

pepper

Crudités, to serve

CRUDITES

2 carrots, peeled and cut into sticks

1 red pepper, deseeded and cut into strips

¹/₂ cucumber, peeled if preferred and cut into strips

4 celery sticks, trimmed and cut into small strips

1 Chop the sun-dried tomatoes, place in a bowl and cover with almost boiling water. Leave for 30 minutes.

2 Place the tomatoes with 2 tablespoons of their soaking liquid in a food processor and blend for 1 minute. Add the olives and process to form a paste, adding more of the soaking liquid if required. Add the Quark and using the pulse button, blend to form a soft consistency, adding the orange or lemon juice at the end.

3 Add pepper to taste and blend for a further 20 seconds. Scrape the dip into a small bowl and sprinkle over a little paprika. Serve with Crudités.

Serving Analysis			
Energy (kcals)	69	Protein (grams)	6.9
Total fat (grams)	1.9	Carbohydrate (grams)	6.2
of which saturated fat (grams)	0.3	of which sugars (grams)	5.9
Fat/100 g product (grams)	**1.3**		

15 minutes, plus 20 minutes' soaking

20 minutes

GI low

Pepper and Mushroom Sauté

Peppers bring a lot of colour to a dish, but they have a reputation for being slightly indigestible. Removing the skins reduces this problem a little. Use either peeled or not, as you prefer.

SERVES 4

10 g/¼ oz porcini mushrooms (ceps)

2 tsp extra virgin olive oil

1 onion, cut into small wedges

2–4 garlic cloves, sliced

115 g/4 oz lean back bacon, fat discarded

1 red pepper, deseeded and cut into strips

1 yellow pepper, deseeded and cut into strips

1 orange pepper, deseeded and cut into strips

150 ml/5 fl oz vegetable stock or red wine

1–2 tbsp shredded fresh basil

pepper

freshly cooked baby new potatoes, to serve (optional)

1 Pick over the mushrooms and place in a small bowl. Cover with hot, not boiling, water and leave for 20 minutes. Drain, reserving the soaking liquid, and set aside.

2 Heat the oil in a large frying pan, add the onion and garlic and cook over a medium heat for 3 minutes, stirring occasionally.

3 Cut the bacon into strips, add to the frying pan and cook for 2 minutes. Add the drained mushrooms with their soaking liquor and the peppers and sauté for 5 minutes, stirring occasionally.

4 Pour in the stock, bring to the boil, then reduce the heat to a simmer and cook for 8–10 minutes, or until the peppers are soft but still retain a bite.

5 Season with pepper to taste, sprinkle with the shredded basil and serve with cooked baby new potatoes, also sprinkled with shredded basil.

Cook's Tip

If you want to peel the peppers, cut each pepper into quarters and discard the seeds and membrane. Place on a foil-lined grill rack. Cook under a preheated hot grill for 5–8 minutes, turning the peppers round as the skins blacken. Leave to cool in a polythene bag for about 10 minutes, or until cool enough to handle. The skins can then easily be peeled off.

Serving Analysis

Energy (kcals)	130	Protein (grams)	7.7
Total fat (grams)	3.9	Carbohydrate (grams)	10.1
of which saturated fat (grams)	1	of which sugars (grams)	8
Fat/100 g product (grams)	**1.8**		

Sweet Potato Blinis

20 minutes

45 minutes

GI low

These blinis are very versatile. Try them for an informal lunch, or as an unusual dinner party starter, or make them smaller and serve as canapés.

SERVES 4–6

115 g/4 oz sweet potatoes, peeled and cut into chunks

1 tsp ground allspice

55 g/2 oz wholemeal flour

1 egg

150 ml/5 fl oz skimmed milk

1 egg white

pepper

FILLING

85 g/3 oz Parma ham, fat discarded

3 tomatoes, thickly sliced

150 ml/5 fl oz 8% fat fromage frais

1 tbsp finely grated lemon rind

1 tbsp chopped fresh parsley

25 g/1 oz rocket leaves

Cook's Tip

Keep the blinis warm either covered with foil in a warm oven or wrapped in a clean tea towel on a plate set over a saucepan of gently simmering water.

1 Cook the sweet potatoes in boiling water over a medium heat for 15 minutes, or until soft. Drain and mash until smooth, then season with pepper to taste and stir in the ground allspice and flour. Place in a mixing bowl.

2 Add the whole egg and beat it into the mashed sweet potatoes, then gradually stir in the milk to give a thick batter consistency. Reserve until required.

3 Prepare the filling. Preheat the grill. Cut the Parma ham into strips. Place the tomatoes on a foil-lined grill rack and, just before serving, cook under the preheated grill for 3–4 minutes, or until hot. Blend the fromage frais with the lemon rind and parsley. Reserve.

4 Whisk the egg white until stiff and stir it into the sweet potato batter. Heat a non-stick frying pan until hot then place 3–4 spoonfuls of the batter in the frying pan and swirl to form a 7.5-cm/3-inch round. Cook for 2–3 minutes, or until set, then turn over and cook for a further 2–3 minutes, or until golden. Keep warm while you cook the remaining batter.

5 Place 2–3 blinis on a plate, top with a little rocket, Parma ham and grilled tomato, spoon over a little of the fromage frais and serve.

Serving Analysis

Energy (kcals)	116	Protein (grams)	9.5
Total fat (grams)	3.3	Carbohydrate (grams)	12.9
of which saturated fat (grams)	1	of which sugars (grams)	4.2
Fat/100 g product (grams)	**2.4**		

20 minutes

16 minutes

GI low

Thai-style Fish Cakes

These fish cakes are extremely easy to make, and provide a tasty and delicious midweek snack. Try serving them with freshly cooked brown basmati rice and an Oriental-style salad.

SERVES 6

400 g/14 oz canned white crabmeat

1–2 fresh bird's eye chillies, to taste, deseeded and finely chopped

6 spring onions, finely shredded

1 courgette, grated

1 carrot, grated

1 small yellow pepper, deseeded and finely shredded

85 g/3 oz fresh beansprouts, rinsed

1 tbsp chopped fresh coriander

1 large egg white

1–2 tbsp sunflower oil

SALSA

1 bird's eye chilli, deseeded and finely chopped

5-cm/2-inch piece cucumber, grated

1 tbsp chopped fresh coriander

1 tbsp lime juice

1 tbsp Thai sweet chilli sauce

1 tbsp peanuts, finely chopped (optional)

TO SERVE

rice salad (optional)

salad (optional)

1 Mix all the fish cake ingredients, except for the egg white and oil, together. Whisk the egg white until frothy and just beginning to stiffen then stir into the crab mixture. Then, using your hands, press about 1–2 tablespoons of the mixture together to form a fish cake. Repeat until 12 fish cakes are formed.

2 Make the salsa by combining all the ingredients except for the peanuts. Spoon into a small bowl, cover and leave for 30 minutes for the flavours to develop. Sprinkle with the peanuts, if using.

3 Heat 1 teaspoon of the oil in a non-stick frying pan over a low heat. Cook the fish cakes in batches for 2 minutes on each side over a medium heat until lightly browned. Take care when turning them over. Remove and drain on kitchen paper. Repeat until all the fish cakes are cooked, using more oil if necessary. Serve with the salsa and with rice and salad, if liked.

Serving Analysis			
Energy (kcals)	170	Protein (grams)	23.1
Total fat (grams)	5.2	Carbohydrate (grams)	8.2
of which saturated fat (grams)	0.8	of which sugars (grams)	7.1
Fat/100 g product (grams)	**1.8**		

8–10 minutes

12 minutes

GI low

Wild Mushroom Omelette

If fresh wild mushrooms are unavailable, look for dried porcini mushrooms (ceps), cover with warm water and soak for 20 minutes, then drain and use.

SERVES 2–4

1 tsp extra virgin olive oil

1 small onion, cut into wedges

2–3 garlic cloves, crushed

85 g/3 oz assorted wild mushrooms, cleaned and cut in half if large

85 g/3 oz closed cup mushrooms, wiped and sliced

1 courgette, trimmed and grated

2 eggs plus 2 egg whites

1 yellow pepper, deseeded, peeled and cut into strips

1 tbsp freshly grated Parmesan cheese (optional)

1 tbsp shredded fresh basil

pepper

TO SERVE

tossed green salad

warm wholemeal bread (optional)

Cook's Tip

If liked, the omelette can be placed under a preheated hot grill for the last 2 minutes of the cooking time in order to brown the cheese.

1 Heat the oil in a large non-stick frying pan and cook the onion and garlic over a very gentle heat for 3 minutes. Cover the frying pan during cooking. Stir occasionally. Add the mushrooms and cook for a further 4–5 minutes, or until the mushrooms have softened slightly. Add the grated courgette.

2 Beat the whole eggs with the egg whites, pepper to taste and 2 tablespoons of water. Pour into the frying pan, increase the heat slightly and cook, drawing the egg into the centre of the pan from the edges with a fork or spatula.

3 When the omelette is set on the base, sprinkle the strips of yellow pepper over it, followed by the Parmesan cheese, if using, and basil. Cook for a further 3–4 minutes, or until set to personal preference.

4 Serve the omelette cut into wedges with a tossed green salad and, if liked, warm chunks of wholemeal bread.

Serving Analysis			
Energy (kcals)	87	Protein (grams)	7.3
Total fat (grams)	4.4	Carbohydrate (grams)	4.8
of which saturated fat (grams)	1.1	of which sugars (grams)	3.5
Fat/100 g product (grams)	**2.5**		

Parma Ham with Melon and Asparagus

15 minutes

5 minutes

GI low

When eating melons it is important that they are ripe, but not over- or under-ripe. When choosing a melon a good indication is to gently press one end – it should yield slightly – and to smell it. Ripe melons will give off a sweet, pleasant aroma. Keep out of the refrigerator for best results.

SERVES 4

225 g/8 oz baby asparagus spears

1 small or ½ medium-sized Galia or Canteloupe melon

55 g/2 oz Parma ham, thinly sliced

150 g/5½ oz bag of mixed salad leaves, such as herb salad with rocket

85 g/3 oz fresh raspberries

1 tbsp freshly shaved Parmesan cheese

1 tbsp balsamic vinegar

2 tbsp orange juice

2 tbsp raspberry vinegar

1 Trim the asparagus, cutting in half if very long. Cook in lightly boiled water over a medium heat for 5 minutes, or until tender. Drain and plunge into cold water then drain again and reserve.

2 Cut the melon in half and scoop out the seeds. Cut into small wedges and cut away the rind. Separate the Parma ham, cut the slices in half and wrap around the melon wedges.

3 Arrange the salad leaves on a large serving platter and place the melon wedges on top together with the asparagus spears.

4 Scatter over the raspberries and Parmesan shavings. Place the vinegars and juice in a screw-top jar and shake until blended. Pour over the salad and serve.

Cook's Tip

To make raspberry vinegar, place 225 g/ 8 oz raspberries in a bowl and cover with 600 ml/1 pint of white wine vinegar. Cover and leave for 24 hours then strain, reserving the vinegar. Place a further 225 g/8 oz of raspberries in a bowl and cover with the strained vinegar. Leave for 24 hours then strain and pour into clean sterilized jars. Screw down tightly and store in a cool dark place.

Serving Analysis

Energy (kcals)	95	Protein (grams)	7.8
Total fat (grams)	3.3	Carbohydrate (grams)	8.7
of which saturated fat (grams)	1.2	of which sugars (grams)	8.6
Fat/100 g product (grams)	**1.2**		

12 minutes

33 minutes

GI low

Barley and Vegetable Potage

Pearl barley seems to have fallen out of fashion, having been ousted by trendier ingredients. Here it is used not only to thicken the potage but also to add flavour.

SERVES 4

1 tsp sunflower oil

1 onion, chopped

2 garlic cloves, crushed

1 carrot, diced

2 celery sticks, chopped

55 g/2 oz pearl barley, rinsed

1.2 litres/2 pints vegetable stock

55 g/2 oz frozen peas

225 g/8 oz green cabbage, outer leaves and hard stalk discarded

pepper

Cook's Tip

Other green vegetables can be used if preferred: try shredded pak choi, curly kale or baby spinach. Adjust the cooking time accordingly.

1 Heat the oil in a large saucepan, add the onion, garlic, carrot and celery and cook over a gentle heat for 5 minutes. Stir occasionally.

2 Sprinkle in the pearl barley and stir well. Pour in the stock and bring to the boil. Cover, reduce the heat to a simmer and cook for 15 minutes. Add the peas and cook for a further 5 minutes.

3 Wash the cabbage and shred finely. Add to the saucepan and cook for 2–3 minutes, or until the cabbage is just tender. Season with pepper to taste and serve immediately.

Serving Analysis			
Energy (kcals)	113	Protein (grams)	4.2
Total fat (grams)	2.0	Carbohydrate (grams)	20.9
of which saturated fat (grams)	0.2	of which sugars (grams)	6.5
Fat/100 g product (grams)	**1.2**		

4

main courses

Chicken in Red Wine

10 minutes

30 minutes

GI low

Don't be tempted to use cheap wine in cooking as it will have an adverse effect on the flavour of the dish. Good-quality food needs good-quality wine.

SERVES 4

4 skinless, boneless chicken breasts

1 tsp extra virgin olive oil

1 onion, cut into small wedges

2–3 garlic cloves, thinly sliced

1 red pepper, deseeded and cut into thin strips

300 ml/10 fl oz chicken stock

150 ml/5 fl oz red wine

1 tbsp black olives, stoned

$1^{1}/_{2}$–2 tbsp cornflour

1 tbsp chopped fresh flat-leaf parsley

pepper

freshly cooked broccoli, to serve

BUTTER BEAN PURÉE

300 g/$10^{1}/_{2}$ oz canned butter beans, drained and rinsed

2 tbsp water or vegetable stock

2 garlic cloves, crushed

4 spring onions, trimmed and chopped

2–3 tbsp vegetable stock

1 To make the Butter Bean Purée, place the butter beans in a non-stick saucepan with the water and garlic cloves. Heat for 3–4 minutes, or until piping hot, drain and mash, then season with pepper. Stir in 4 trimmed and chopped spring onions and the stock.

2 Heat the oil in a large non-stick frying pan and seal the chicken over a medium heat until browned all over. Remove and reserve.

3 Add the onion and garlic to the frying pan and cook over a medium heat for 3 minutes, stirring frequently. Return the chicken to the frying pan together with the red pepper strips, the stock and the red wine. Season with pepper to taste.

4 Bring to the boil, reduce the heat to a simmer, cover and cook for 15 minutes, turning the chicken over halfway through the cooking time. Add the olives and cook for a further 3–5 minutes, or until the chicken is thoroughly cooked.

5 Blend the cornflour with 3 tablespoons of water to a smooth paste. Stir into the frying pan and cook, stirring, until the liquid thickens. Sprinkle with the parsley and serve with the Butter Bean Purée and broccoli.

Serving Analysis			
Energy (kcals)	193	Protein (grams)	25.3
Total fat (grams)	2.8	Carbohydrate (grams)	11.7
of which saturated fat (grams)	0.5	of which sugars (grams)	3.5
Fat/100 g product (grams)	**1.3**		

15 minutes, plus 30 minutes' marinating

6–8 minutes

GI low

Griddled Scallops with Bacon

Scallops are far more readily available now than in the past, as most of those on sale are farmed. Look out for king scallops, which are larger than the queen scallops. Choose ones that still retain their coral, the orange piece that is attached.

SERVES 4

8–12 large scallops with corals

2 tbsp orange juice

1 tbsp light soy sauce

8–12 lean back bacon rashers, fat discarded

100 g/3½ oz mixed salad leaves, including small beetroot leaves and mizuna

pepper

TO SERVE

balsamic vinegar

warm Granary bread (optional)

Cook's Tip

If liked, add some strips of peeled yellow pepper and some halved cherry tomatoes to the salad and replace the bread with baby new potatoes.

1 Lightly rinse the scallops and remove the dark vein if necessary. Place in a shallow dish. Blend the orange juice and soy sauce and pour over the scallops. Season with pepper. Cover and leave in the refrigerator for 30 minutes. Drain.

2 Lightly stretch the bacon rashers with the back of a knife. Cut in half. Wrap two halves round each scallop. Thread onto small wooden skewers allowing a little space between each (this will ensure that the scallops cook evenly).

3 Heat a griddle pan until smoking then cook the bacon-wrapped scallops for 6–8 minutes, or until cooked. Turn the scallops frequently as they cook.

4 Arrange the salad leaves on serving platters. Remove the scallops from the skewers and place on top of the salad leaves. Drizzle with a little balsamic vinegar and serve with warm Granary bread.

Serving Analysis			
Energy (kcals)	113	Protein (grams)	18.3
Total fat (grams)	3.1	Carbohydrate (grams)	3.1
of which saturated fat (grams)	1.1	of which sugars (grams)	1.4
Fat/100 g product (grams)	**2.7**		

Warm Beef Niçoise

Ideal to serve when entertaining friends or family at a summer lunch party or an impromptu dinner party.

Cook's Tip

The steaks can be cooked either under a preheated hot grill or barbecue. The cooking time will be the same.

SERVES 4

4 fillet steaks, about 115 g/4 oz each, fat discarded

2 tbsp red wine vinegar

2 tbsp orange juice

2 tsp ready-made English mustard

2 eggs

175 g/6 oz baby new potatoes

115 g/4 oz French beans, trimmed

175 g/6 oz mixed salad leaves, such as baby spinach, rocket and mizuna

1 yellow pepper, peeled, skinned and cut into strips

175 g/6 oz cherry tomatoes, halved

black olives, stoned, to garnish (optional)

2 tsp extra virgin olive oil

pepper

1 Place the steaks in a shallow dish. Blend the vinegar with 1 tablespoon of orange juice and 1 teaspoon of mustard. Pour over the steaks, cover and leave in the refrigerator for at least 30 minutes. Turn over halfway through the marinating time.

2 Place the eggs in a pan and cover with cold water. Bring to the boil, then reduce the heat to a simmer and cook for 10 minutes. Remove and plunge the eggs into cold water. Once cold, shell and reserve.

3 Meanwhile, place the potatoes in a saucepan and cover with cold water. Bring to the boil, cover and simmer for 15 minutes, or until tender when pierced with a fork. Drain and reserve.

4 Bring a saucepan of water to the boil. Add the beans, cover and simmer for 5–8 minutes, or until tender. Drain, plunge into cold water then drain again and reserve. Meanwhile, arrange all the vegetables on top of the salad leaves together with the yellow pepper, cherry tomatoes and olives, if using. Blend the remaining orange juice and mustard with the olive oil and reserve.

5 Heat a griddle pan until smoking. Drain the steaks and cook for 3–5 minutes on each side or according to personal preference. Slice the steaks and arrange on top of the salad, then pour over the dressing and serve.

Serving Analysis			
Energy (kcals)	281	Protein (grams)	30.8
Total fat (grams)	11.3	Carbohydrate (grams)	13.5
of which saturated fat (grams)	4.3	of which sugars (grams)	6.6
Fat/100 g product (grams)	3		

Sole and Orange with Wilted Chard

10 minutes

50 minutes

GI low

This makes a good lunch dish, as it is both quick and easy to prepare and cook, leaving you plenty of time to chat to your guests.

SERVES 4

8 sole fillets

1½ tbsp finely grated orange rind

280 g/10 oz chard, thoroughly rinsed

6 spring onions, trimmed and finely chopped

2 tbsp orange juice

1 tbsp lemon juice (optional)

450 g/1 lb baby new potatoes

280 g/10 oz baby carrots, scrubbed

175 g/6 oz peeled prawns, thawed if frozen

pepper

Cook's Tip

Take care not to overcook the parcels once you have added the prawns or the prawns will be tough and tasteless. They just need reheating.

1 Preheat the oven to 180°C/350°F/Gas Mark 4. Lightly rinse the sole fillets and pat dry with kitchen paper. Mix half the orange rind with some pepper and sprinkle over each fillet. Reserve. Remove the white ribs from the chard and shred the green leaves. Cut out 4 squares of baking paper or foil, 20-cm/8-inch in diameter, and divide the leaves between the sheets. Place 2 sole fillets on top of each, sprinkle over two-thirds of the spring onions and a little orange juice then fold the paper over to form a parcel. Place in a baking tin. Cook in the oven for 10 minutes. Cut the white ribs of the chard into small pieces, rinse and cook in lightly boiling water with the lemon juice for 15–20 minutes, or until tender. Drain and keep warm.

2 Meanwhile, cook the potatoes in boiling water over a medium heat for 15 minutes, or until tender when pierced with a fork. Drain and lightly crush with a potato masher. Stir in the remaining spring onions and season with pepper. Keep warm. At the same time, cook the carrots in boiling water for 10–15 minutes, or until tender when pierced with a fork, drain and sprinkle with the remaining rind. Keep warm.

3 Remove the fish parcels from the oven and carefully open them. Scatter the peeled prawns over the fish. Fold the parcels again and return to the oven for a further 5 minutes. Remove and place a parcel on each plate. Serve with the cooked white chard ribs, and the potatoes and carrots.

Serving Analysis			
Energy (kcals)	256	Protein (grams)	32.3
Total fat (grams)	3.2	Carbohydrate (grams)	25.9
of which saturated fat (grams)	0.5	of which sugars (grams)	8.8
Fat/100 g product (grams)	0.7		

15 minutes

25 minutes

GI low

Cod Loin with Herb Crust

This is a perfect supper dish for the whole family. Other white fish can be used for this recipe, if preferred. If you use sole, plaice or halibut, cook for slightly less time.

SERVES 4

Cook's Tip

Take care not to overcook the fish or it will be dry. Pierce the salmon with a sharp knife: if it goes in easily with no resistance the fish is cooked.

4 pieces cod loin, about 115 g/4 oz each

4 garlic cloves

1 tbsp finely grated orange rind

2 tbsp chopped fresh parsley

2 tbsp chopped fresh dill

2 tbsp chopped fresh tarragon

4 tbsp orange juice

4 large tomatoes

pepper

TO SERVE

butter bean purée

freshly cooked green beans

1 Preheat the oven to 200°C/400°F/Gas Mark 6. Lightly rinse the fish and pat dry with kitchen paper. Crush 2 of the garlic cloves and mix with the orange rind, the herbs and a little pepper then press one-quarter of the herb mixture onto each piece of fish. Place the fish in an ovenproof dish and pour the orange juice round them.

2 Rinse and dry the tomatoes and cut in half. Cut the remaining garlic cloves into thin slivers and insert 3–4 slivers into each tomato half. Place in an ovenproof dish.

3 Place the fish in the oven and cook for 10 minutes then add the tomatoes and cook with the fish for a further 10 minutes, or until the fish is cooked.

4 Serve with butter bean purée, the roasted tomatoes and green beans.

Serving Analysis			
Energy (kcals)	107	Protein (grams)	21.9
Total fat (grams)	0.9	Carbohydrate (grams)	3
of which saturated fat (grams)	0.1	of which sugars (grams)	1.5
Fat/100 g product (grams)	**0.6**		

15 minutes, plus 30 minutes' marinating

40 minutes

GI low

Turkey with Roasted Vegetables

Turkey is a good choice when trying to keep down the fat content of your diet, as it is one of the leanest meats. Don't serve it only for Christmas – try using some of the many various cuts that are now readily available.

SERVES 4

4 skinless turkey breast fillets, about 115 g/4 oz each

1 fresh red chilli, deseeded

4 garlic cloves, peeled

1 onion, cut into wedges

1 courgette, cut into chunks

1 red pepper, deseeded and cut into thick strips

1 yellow pepper, deseeded and cut into thick wedges

1–2 tbsp extra virgin olive oil

225 g/8 oz vine-ripened cherry or small plum tomatoes

1 tbsp shredded fresh basil

pepper

280 g/10 oz freshly cooked tagliatelle, to serve

1 Preheat the oven to 190°C/375°F/Gas Mark 5. Lightly rinse the turkey breast fillets and pat dry with kitchen paper. Finely chop the chilli, crush 2 of the garlic cloves, mix together then rub over the turkey. Place on a plate, cover loosely with baking paper and leave in the refrigerator for 30 minutes.

2 Cut the remaining garlic cloves in half, place in a roasting tin with the remaining prepared vegetables except for the tomatoes and drizzle over one tablespoon of the oil. Grind over some pepper.

3 Roast in the preheated oven for 15 minutes, turning the vegetables over occasionally. Place the turkey steaks on top and continue to roast for 15 minutes, then add the tomatoes and roast for a further 10 minutes, or until the turkey is thoroughly cooked. Sprinkle with the shredded basil and serve with freshly cooked tagliatelle.

Serving Analysis			
Energy (kcals)	201	Protein (grams)	31.1
Total fat (grams)	4.3	Carbohydrate (grams)	10
of which saturated fat (grams)	0.9	of which sugars (grams)	8
Fat/100 g product (grams)	**1.3**		

Aromatic Chicken Parcels

15 minutes

50 minutes

GI low

The aromatic flavours of the East can be used to great effect in both savoury and sweet dishes. Here the chicken is delicately spiced and enhanced by the use of spices also in the rice.

SERVES 4

4 skinless, boneless chicken breasts, about 115 g/4 oz each

1 tsp or fine spray extra virgin olive oil

1 courgette, trimmed

1 carrot

1 celery stick, trimmed

1 small red pepper, deseeded

2 cinnamon sticks, broken in half

10 cardamom pods, lightly cracked

4 tbsp white wine

1 tbsp chopped fresh coriander

175 g/6 oz brown basmati rice

few saffron strands

pepper

Cook's Tip

Fish such as salmon steaks, swordfish steaks or plaice fillets can be used in place of the chicken. The cooking times may need to be adjusted.

1 Preheat the oven to 190°C/375°F/Gas Mark 5. Cut 4 square sheets of baking paper, 20 cm/8 inches in size. Lightly rinse the chicken and pat dry with kitchen paper. Heat a non-stick frying pan, add the oil then brown the chicken on all sides. Reserve.

2 Cut all the vegetables into thin strips. In the centre of each square of baking paper place one quarter of the vegetable strips with a chicken breast on top. Place half a cinnamon stick and 2 of the cardamom pods on each chicken breast. Pour over 1 tablespoon of wine, season with a little pepper and add a little chopped coriander. Fold over to encase the vegetables and chicken.

3 Place the chicken parcels in a large baking tin and cook in the preheated oven for 20 minutes, or until thoroughly cooked. Remove the parcels from the oven and place each one on a serving plate, allowing each person to appreciate the aroma as they open their own parcel.

4 Meanwhile, rinse the rice then place in a saucepan with the remaining cardamom pods and the saffron strands. Cover with water, bring to the boil then cover, reduce the heat to a simmer and cook for 20–25 minutes, or until tender. Drain, place in a warmed serving bowl and serve with the chicken.

Serving Analysis			
Energy (kcals)	335	Protein (grams)	32
Total fat (grams)	2.6	Carbohydrate (grams)	40.5
of which saturated fat (grams)	0.5	of which sugars (grams)	5.3
Fat/100 g product (grams)	0.9		

Griddled Duck with Apricot Relish

Whether you use a griddle pan or a griddling machine, ensure that it is piping hot so that the food does not stick – there is no need to use any oil or fat.

SERVES 4

4 boneless duck breasts

300 ml/10 fl oz pint orange juice

2 garlic cloves, crushed

2 tbsp balsamic vinegar

175 g/6 oz Puy lentils

1 tbsp orange zest

orange wedges, to garnish

cherry tomato salad, to serve

APRICOT RELISH

1 onion, thinly sliced

55 g/2 oz dried apricots, finely chopped

1 tsp dark muscovado sugar

1 Remove the skin and fat from the duck and rinse lightly. Pat dry with kitchen paper, then make 3 diagonal slashes across each. Place in a dish then blend together 2 tablespoons of the orange juice, the garlic and 1 tablespoon of the vinegar and pour over the duck. Cover loosely and leave in the refrigerator for 30 minutes.

2 To make the relish, sauté the onion in a non-stick saucepan over a gentle heat for 5 minutes, stirring occasionally. Add the apricots and 150 ml/5 fl oz of the orange juice then simmer for 10 minutes. Stir in the sugar and the remaining vinegar and simmer for 5 minutes, or until the mixture has reduced and thickened. Add a little more orange juice if the consistency becomes too dry and reduce the heat a little.

3 Rinse the lentils then place in a saucepan with the remaining orange juice and zest and sufficient water to cover. Bring to the boil, cover and simmer for 30 minutes, or until tender. Meanwhile, heat a griddle pan until smoking then drain the duck thoroughly and cook in the pan for 4–5 minutes on each side, or until cooked to personal preference. Cut the duck into thin slices and drain the cooked lentils, then transfer to warmed serving plates. Garnish with orange wedges and serve with a little relish and the cherry tomato salad.

Serving Analysis			
Energy (kcals)	349	Protein (grams)	34.7
Total fat (grams)	8.3	Carbohydrate (grams)	40.5
of which saturated fat (grams)	1.6	of which sugars (grams)	15.8
Fat/100 g product (grams)	**3**		

5

vegetables and vegetarian

Aubergine Medley

15 minutes

25 minutes

GI low

Aubergines are a very versatile vegetable and can be served in a variety of ways. They can also be made into delicious dips, and the roasted flesh is an ideal thickening agent for casseroles.

SERVES 4

1 large aubergine, weighing about 280 g/10 oz, sliced

1 tbsp extra virgin olive oil

1 onion, cut into wedges

2–4 garlic cloves, cut in half

1 red pepper, deseeded, skinned and chopped

1 yellow pepper, deseeded, skinned and chopped

200 ml/7 fl oz vegetable stock

115 g/4 oz button mushrooms

225 g/8 oz baby spinach leaves, rinsed

85 g/3 oz goat's cheese, sliced

wholemeal or Granary bread, to serve

Cook's Tip

If baby spinach is unavailable, use leaf spinach and shred before using.

1 Heat the oil in a large frying pan and add the aubergine with the onion and garlic. Cook over a very gentle heat for 10 minutes, stirring frequently, then add the peppers. Pour in the stock, bring to the boil then reduce the heat, cover and simmer for 10 minutes.

2 Add the mushrooms and continue to simmer for 5 minutes then stir in the spinach and cook, uncovered, stirring occasionally until the spinach has begun to wilt.

3 Place the goat's cheese slices on top then heat for 1–2 minutes, or until the cheese begins to melt, then serve immediately with chunks of wholemeal or Granary bread.

Serving Analysis			
Energy (kcals)	132	Protein (grams)	7.2
Total fat (grams)	7.5	Carbohydrate (grams)	9.6
of which saturated fat (grams)	2.8	of which sugars (grams)	7.9
Fat/100 g product (grams)	**2.7**		

15 minutes

2 hours

GI low

Stuffed Marrow

Although marrows seem to have gone out of fashion, they are available virtually throughout the year, from supermarkets, farm shops or farmers' markets, and they are also really easy to grow yourself.

SERVES 4

85 g/3 oz green lentils

1 tsp extra virgin olive oil

1 onion, finely chopped

2–3 garlic cloves, crushed

1 celery stick, chopped

1 carrot, grated

1 tbsp chopped fresh rosemary

1 egg white, beaten

200 ml/7 fl oz vegetable stock

1 marrow, weighing 900 g/2 lb 2 beef tomatoes, thickly sliced

25 g/1 oz mature half-fat Cheddar cheese, grated

pepper

freshly cooked carrots, to serve

Cook's Tip

If time is short, use canned lentils that are already cooked. Whole peppers, whole halved courgettes or large onions could be used in place of the marrow.

1 Preheat the oven to 180°C/350°F/Gas Mark 4. Rinse the lentils, place in a saucepan, cover with water and bring to the boil and cook for 10 minutes. Reduce the heat, cover and simmer for 35 minutes, or until soft. Drain thoroughly and reserve.

2 Heat the oil in a saucepan and sauté the onion, garlic, celery and carrot for 5 minutes, or until softened. Stir in the lentils with the rosemary, and season with pepper to taste. Remove from the heat and add the egg white and sufficient stock to moisten the mixture.

3 Peel the marrow if preferred and cut into 5-cm/2-inch thick rings. Remove the seeds then place in an ovenproof dish large enough to hold all the rings. Stuff the hollows with the lentil mixture. Place a tomato slice on each ring, pour round the remaining stock and cover with foil.

4 Cook in the preheated oven for 1 hour, or until the marrow feels tender when pierced with the tip of a sharp knife. Remove the foil and sprinkle the tomato with the grated cheese. Return to the oven for a further 5 minutes. Serve with the freshly cooked carrots.

Serving Analysis			
Energy (kcals)	153	Protein (grams)	10.6
Total fat (grams)	3.2	Carbohydrate (grams)	22
of which saturated fat (grams)	0.8	of which sugars (grams)	9.9
Fat/100 g product (grams)	**0.8**		

20 minutes, plus cooling time

1 hour 10 minutes

GI low

Lentil & Asparagus Quiche

Red lentils are best for this quiche base and can be easily moulded into the flan tin.

Cook's Tip

If possible use a smooth-sided tin, as this will make the quiche easier to remove.

SERVES 6

225 g/8 oz red lentils

1 tbsp chopped fresh basil

3 egg whites plus 2 whole eggs

115 g/4 oz baby asparagus spears

1 red pepper, deseeded, skinned and cut into strips

1 orange pepper, deseeded, skinned and cut into strips

4 spring onions, trimmed and diagonally sliced

8 black olives, stoned

65 g/1½ oz feta cheese (drained weight), crumbled

8 tbsp 8% fat fromage frais

pepper

TO SERVE

salad

Granary bread

1 Preheat the oven to 190°C/375°F/Gas Mark 5. Rinse the lentils, place in a saucepan and cover with cold water. Bring to the boil, cover, reduce the heat to a simmer and cook for 12–14 minutes, or until soft. Drain off any excess water and leave to cool. When cool, stir in the pepper to taste, the basil and 2 of the egg whites. Mix well then press into a 20-cm/8-inch loose-based flan tin. Bake in the oven for 25–30 minutes, or until the base feels dry. Remove and reserve.

2 Trim the asparagus spears to fit the quiche then cook in lightly boiling water for 4 minutes. Drain then plunge into cold water, drain again and arrange in the base of the quiche. Cover with the pepper strips, the spring onions, olives and cheese.

3 Beat the 2 whole eggs with the remaining egg white and pepper to taste then stir in the fromage frais. Spoon over the asparagus mixture then bake in the preheated oven for 25–30 minutes, or until set. Serve with salad and warm chunks of Granary bread.

Serving Analysis			
Energy (kcals)	198	Protein (grams)	18.2
Total fat (grams)	2.3	Carbohydrate (grams)	28
of which saturated fat (grams)	1.1	of which sugars (grams)	7.4
Fat/100 g product (grams)	1.1		

Oriental Stir-fried Vegetables

15 minutes

8 minutes

GI low

This recipe can be used as an accompaniment or as a main meal. If using as a main meal, add either some diced tofu for vegetarians or strips of lean meat or fish for others.

SERVES 4

2 tsp sunflower oil

2 lemongrass stalks, outer leaves removed and chopped

2–4 garlic cloves, crushed

1 bird's eye chilli, deseeded and chopped

1 tbsp grated root ginger

1 red pepper, deseeded and cut into strips

1 yellow pepper, deseeded and cut into strips

1 orange pepper, deseeded and cut into strips

115 g/4 oz courgettes, cut into strips

6 spring onions, diagonally sliced

115 g/4 oz pak choi, thoroughly washed, drained and shredded

85 g/3 oz beansprouts

1 tbsp light soy sauce

1 tbsp medium sherry

freshly cooked brown basmati rice or Japanese soba noodles, to serve

Cook's Tip

It is important to preheat the wok before adding the oil. This ensures that the food does not stick. When stir-frying use a large spatula and stir constantly, tossing the food around in the wok.

1 Preheat a wok, then when hot add the sunflower oil and heat for a further 15 seconds. Add the lemongrass, garlic, chilli and root ginger and stir-fry over a high heat for 1 minute. Add the pepper and courgette strips and stir-fry for 2 minutes.

2 Add the spring onions and continue to stir-fry for a further 2 minutes before adding the pak choi and beansprouts. Stir-fry for 1 minute.

3 Blend the soy sauce with the sherry and add to the wok. Stir-fry for 1 minute, or until the vegetables are just cooked. Serve with freshly cooked basmati rice or Japanese soba noodles.

Serving Analysis			
Energy (kcals)	81	Protein (grams)	3.7
Total fat (grams)	2.3	Carbohydrate (grams)	11.2
of which saturated fat (grams)	0.3	of which sugars (grams)	9.3
Fat/100 g product (grams)	**1**		

Warm Bean Salad

This salad is delicious whether served warm or cold. If you wish to serve it warm, prepare all the ingredients ahead of time, then when you are ready to eat, it will be no effort at all to cook the salad and serve it in minutes.

SERVES 6

1 tsp olive oil

1 red onion, peeled and finely chopped

2–3 garlic cloves, peeled and chopped

1 red chilli, deseeded and chopped

1 red pepper, deseeded and skinned

1 orange pepper, deseeded and skinned

300 g/10^{1}/$_2$ oz canned red kidney beans, drained and thoroughly rinsed

300 g/10^{1}/$_2$ oz can black eyed beans, drained and thoroughly rinsed

300 g/10^{1}/$_2$ oz can flageolet beans, drained and thoroughly rinsed

200 ml/7 fl oz passata or tomato juice

1 tbsp sweet chilli sauce

100 g/3^{1}/$_2$ oz cherry tomatoes, halved

1 tbsp freshly chopped coriander

salt and pepper

warm strips of pitta bread, to serve

Cook's Tip

If liked, pass half the bean mixture through a food processor to form a chunky purée (you may need a little extra passata when blending). Return to the saucepan with the remaining whole beans and heat through gently.

1 Heat the oil in a large saucepan and gently sauté the onion, garlic and chilli for 3 minutes, stirring frequently. Cut the red and yellow peppers into thin strips and thoroughly drain the beans.

2 Add the peppers and beans to the saucepan together with the passata and sweet chilli sauce and season to taste. Bring to the boil, reduce the heat and cook for 10 minutes, or until the beans are piping hot. Add the halved tomatoes and heat gently for 2 minutes. Spoon into a serving bowl and sprinkle with the chopped coriander. Serve warm with strips of pitta bread.

Serving Analysis			
Energy (kcals)	128	Protein (grams)	8.0
Total fat (grams)	1.2	Carbohydrate (grams)	17.4
of which saturated fat (grams)	0.3	of which sugars (grams)	7.1
Fat/100 g product (grams)	0.7		

Fennel & Lentil Loaf

This is a versatile vegetarian main course, which meat eaters will also enjoy. It is equally good eaten hot or cold.

SERVES 6

225 g/8 oz red split lentils

1 small fennel bulb, trimmed and cut into thin wedges

1 yellow pepper, deseeded and skinned

1 red pepper, deseeded and skinned

1 small onion, finely chopped

2 garlic cloves, crushed

1 tbsp chopped fresh coriander

55 g/2 oz half-fat Cheddar cheese, grated

1 egg

freshly cooked cabbage, to serve

SAUCE

2 red peppers, deseeded and skinned

1 small onion, finely chopped

300 ml/10 fl oz vegetable stock

1 tbsp tomato purée

pepper

1 Preheat the oven to 190°C/375°F/Gas Mark 5. Line the base of a 900-g/2-lb loaf tin with a piece of non-stick baking paper. Rinse the lentils, place in a saucepan, cover with water and cook for 25–30 minutes, or until soft, then drain thoroughly.

2 Meanwhile, cook the fennel in boiling water for 5 minutes, then drain and place in a bowl. Cut the yellow pepper and red pepper into strips then add to the fennel wedges and reserve.

3 Add the onion to the lentil mixture together with the garlic, coriander and cheese. Season with pepper to taste. Stir in the egg and mix well. Place half of the mixture in the base of the tin, then arrange the fennel wedges and pepper strips on top. Spoon the remaining lentil mixture on top and smooth the top. Bake in the preheated oven for 45–50 minutes, or until the top of the loaf feels firm.

4 Make the sauce by simmering the remaining peppers and onion in the stock for 10 minutes, or until very soft. Stir in the tomato purée and simmer for a further 5 minutes. Pass through a food processor then, if a smooth sauce is preferred, rub through a fine sieve. Season with pepper to taste then serve with the cooked loaf and freshly cooked cabbage.

Serving Analysis			
Energy (kcals)	207	Protein (grams)	15
Total fat (grams)	3.6	Carbohydrate (grams)	30.5
of which saturated fat (grams)	1.3	of which sugars (grams)	8.9
Fat/100 g product (grams)	**1.8**		

Red Cabbage Slaw

20 minutes

no cooking required

GI low

Ideal for any occasion, as part of a buffet or even eaten on its own as a lunchtime snack, this can also be turned into a main meal salad by simply adding a little cheese or a few nuts.

SERVES 6

450 g/1 lb red cabbage

1 eating apple

4 tbsp orange juice

1 large carrot, peeled and grated

1 red onion, peeled and cut into tiny wedges

175 g/6 oz cherry tomatoes, halved

7.5-cm/3-inch piece cucumber, peeled if preferred and diced

55 g/2 oz fresh dates, stoned and chopped

1 tbsp extra virgin olive oil

1 tbsp chopped fresh flat-leaf parsley

pepper

Cook's Tip

Vary the ingredients used – try a mix of both red and hard white cabbage. Add some skinned chopped peppers, or radishes, grated celeriac or shredded pak choi.

1 Discard the outer leaves and hard central core from the cabbage and shred finely. Wash thoroughly in plenty of cold water then shake dry and place in a salad bowl.

2 Core the apple and chop, toss in 1 tablespoon of the orange juice then add to the salad bowl together with the carrot, onion, tomatoes, cucumbers and dates.

3 Place the remaining orange juice in a screw-top jar, add the oil, parsley and pepper and shake until blended. Pour the dressing over the salad, toss lightly and serve.

Serving Analysis			
Energy (kcals)	78	Protein (grams)	1.8
Total fat (grams)	2.4	Carbohydrate (grams)	13.3
of which saturated fat (grams)	0.3	of which sugars (grams)	12.6
Fat/100 g product (grams)	**1.1**		

15 minutes

5 minutes

GI low

Asparagus, Spinach & Cherry Tomato Salad

Asparagus is now readily available throughout the year and, although it is expensive, only a small quantity is required for this recipe and it is well worth the expense. Look for home-grown asparagus during May and early June.

Cook's Tip

If liked, use fine French beans in place of the asparagus. Prepare as for the asparagus, discarding the stalk end of the bean.

SERVES 4

175 g/6 oz baby or fine asparagus spears

225 g/8 oz baby spinach leaves

2 heads chicory

8 spring onions, trimmed and chopped

1 small bunch radishes, trimmed and halved

225 g/8 oz cherry tomatoes, halved

400 g/14 oz canned red kidney beans, drained and rinsed

DRESSING

1 tbsp extra virgin olive oil

3 tbsp orange juice

1 tsp wholegrain mustard

1 tbsp balsamic vinegar

1 Trim the asparagus spears if necessary then cook in gently simmering water for 3–5 minutes, or until just tender. Drain, plunge into cold water then drain again and reserve. Lightly rinse the spinach leaves and shake dry. Arrange in a salad bowl or on a large platter.

2 Divide the chicory into leaves, rinse and shake dry. Arrange with the drained asparagus on top of the spinach.

3 Place the spring onions, the radishes, cherry tomatoes and red kidney beans in a bowl and toss lightly. Arrange on the salad with the asparagus and chicory. Place all the dressing ingredients together in a screw-top jar and shake vigorously. Pour over the salad and serve.

Serving Analysis			
Energy (kcals)	175	Protein (grams)	11
Total fat (grams)	4.6	Carbohydrate (grams)	23.7
of which saturated fat (grams)	0.7	of which sugars (grams)	9.1
Fat/100 g product (grams)	**1.4**		

Beetroot with Orange

The combination of beetroot and orange may seem a little strange but it is absolutely delicious. Make sure to use fresh beetroot rather than beetroot that has been pickled in vinegar.

SERVES 4

450 g/1 lb cooked fresh beetroot

1 small orange

25 g/1 oz half-fat Cheddar cheese

few mixed salad leaves

1–2 tsp extra virgin olive oil

1 tbsp snipped fresh chives

pepper

1 Peel the beetroot, discarding the root and skin, then cut into small dice or slices. Peel the orange over a bowl to catch the juice, then divide into segments, taking care to discard the bitter white pith and as much of the membrane as possible. Cut the segments in half. Cut the cheese into small pieces.

2 Place the salad leaves in a serving bowl. Arrange the beetroot and orange segments on top then scatter over the cheese.

3 Drizzle over the oil, sprinkle with the chives and the reserved orange juice, and season to taste with pepper. Serve immediately.

Cook's Tip

Raw beetroot can be cooked in the oven, on the hob or in the microwave. Cut off the leaves about 2.5 cm/ 1 inch from the top of the beetroot. Scrub well, taking care not to damage the skin. To cook in the oven, wrap the beetroot in foil and cook in a preheated oven at 190°C/375°F/ Gas Mark 5 for 1 hour, or until cooked. To cook on the hob, put the beetroot in a saucepan and cover with cold water. Bring to the boil, cover, reduce the heat to a simmer and cook for 1 hour, or until tender. To microwave, place the beetroot in a bowl, cover with microwave film that is lightly pierced, and cook on High for 14–20 minutes, or until cooked. Leave until cool enough to handle.

Serving Analysis

Energy (kcals)	72	Protein (grams)	4.2
Total fat (grams)	1.9	Carbohydrate (grams)	11.2
of which saturated fat (grams)	0.7	of which sugars (grams)	10.6
Fat/100 g product (grams)	1.2		

6

desserts and bakes

Sparkling Melon Cups

15 minutes

10 minutes, plus
2 hours' setting

GI medium

This is a perfect dessert to serve on a hot summer's day, either for an
informal lunch or a more formal dinner party.

SERVES 4

450 ml/16 fl oz Champagne or sparkling
   white wine

1–2 tsp clear honey, or to taste

1 sachet (5 g/¼ oz) gelatine

3 tbsp brandy or Cointreau, or use
   extra wine

2 wedges assorted melons, such as Galia,
   Ogen or Cantaloupe

100 g/3½ oz fresh raspberries

1 Pour the Champagne into a heavy-based saucepan, add the honey then sprinkle in
the gelatine. Place over a gentle heat and bring to the boil, whisking throughout.
Remove and continue to whisk for 2 minutes, or until the gelatine has completely
dissolved. Stir in the brandy, pour into a jug and leave until cold.

2 Discard the skin and any seeds from the melon wedges and cut into small dice.
Arrange with the raspberries in wide-rimmed cocktail or similar glasses, or in
individual glass dishes.

3 Once the jelly is cold, pour over the fruit and leave in the refrigerator for 2 hours,
or until set.

Cook's Tip

For a change, cut the
melon into thin wedges
and arrange in
alternating colours in
a mould or 900-g/2-lb
loaf tin. Pour over the
cold jelly and cover with
clingfilm and clean
weights and leave to
set. Other fruits can
be added or used. Do
not use citrus and kiwi
fruits, however – these
will stop the jelly
from setting.

Serving Analysis			
Energy (kcals)	128	Protein (grams)	2.2
Total fat (grams)	0.1	Carbohydrate (grams)	11.6
of which saturated fat (grams)	0	of which sugars (grams)	11.6
Fat/100 g product (grams)	**0.1**		

Carrot Cake

Carrot cake is a perennial, universal favourite that is ideal for any occasion. When you are looking for a treat, look no further than this recipe.

MAKES 12 SQUARES

300 g/10½ oz self-raising wholemeal flour

2½ tsp baking powder

1 tsp ground cinnamon

½ tsp mixed spice

25 g/1 oz wheat bran

85 g/3 oz light muscovado sugar

115 g/4 oz carrots, grated

350 g/12 oz eating apples, peeled, cored and grated

85 g/3oz raisins

150 g/5½ oz dried apricots, finely chopped

1 egg, beaten

1 egg white

20 ml/4 tsp sunflower oil

125 ml/4 fl oz orange juice

1 tbsp flaked almonds (optional)

1 Preheat the oven to 180°C/350°F/Gas Mark 4. Lightly oil and line the base of a 23 x 33-cm/9 x 13-inch oblong baking tin with non-stick baking paper. Sift the flour, baking powder and spices into a mixing bowl, adding any bran residue left in the sieve. Stir in the wheat bran and the sugar. Add the carrots, grated apple, raisins and apricots and stir well.

2 Beat the egg and egg white together and add to the mixture together with sufficient oil to give a soft dropping consistency. Spoon into the prepared tin and smooth the top.

3 Scatter over the flaked almonds, if using, and bake in the oven for 30–35 minutes or until risen and the top springs back when touched lightly with a clean finger. Remove from the oven and allow to cool before cutting into squares and serving.

Serving Analysis			
Energy (kcals)	147	Protein (grams)	4
Total fat (grams)	2.3	Carbohydrate (grams)	29.6
of which saturated fat (grams)	0.3	of which sugars (grams)	17.4
Fat/100 g product (grams)	**2.7**		

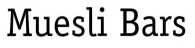

Muesli Bars

These bars are ideal for lunch boxes and will give a lift to flagging energy.

Cook's Tip

Using unrefined sugar means that less sugar can be used as it is sweeter than refined, with more depth of flavour.

MAKES 12 BARS

85 g/3 oz light muscovado sugar

2 tsp baking powder

1 tsp ground cinnamon

½ tsp ground ginger

225 g/8 oz rolled oats

85 g/3 oz raisins

55 g/2 oz pecan nuts, chopped

85 g/3 oz dried cranberries

1 egg

1 egg white

150 ml/5 fl oz clear unsweetened apple juice

1 Preheat the oven to 200°C/400°F/Gas Mark 6. Line a shallow 20 x 30-cm/ 8 x 12-inch baking tin with non-stick baking paper. Mix the sugar, baking powder and spices in a large bowl. Stir in the oats, raisins, pecan nuts and cranberries. Beat the egg and egg white together, then add sufficient apple juice to the mixture to bring the mixture together. Mix well.

2 Press into the prepared tin, smoothing the top with a palette knife, and bake in the preheated oven for 15–20 minutes, or until lightly browned. Remove from the oven and leave until cold before cutting into bars.

Serving Analysis			
Energy (kcals)	76	Protein (grams)	1.9
Total fat (grams)	1.1	Carbohydrate (grams)	15.8
of which saturated fat (grams)	0.2	of which sugars (grams)	11.6
Fat/100 g product (grams)	**3**		

Berry Granita

This is especially good on long hot summer days when you need something to help you cool down.

SERVES 4

450 g/1 lb mixed summer berries, such as raspberries, strawberries and blueberries

125 ml/4 fl oz red wine

125 ml/4 fl oz clear unsweetened apple juice

1–2 tsp clear honey, or to taste

2 tbsp kirsch or Cointreau, or use extra apple juice

TO DECORATE

few fresh mint sprigs

extra berries

Cook's Tip

Chill the glasses for 10 minutes before using. Remember to return the freezer to its normal setting.

1 Either turn your freezer to rapid freeze 2 hours before you want to freeze or place the bowl of an ice cream maker in the freezer overnight. Pick over the berries, hulling any as necessary and cutting any large fruits in half. Rinse lightly.

2 Place the fruits in a heavy-based saucepan and add the wine, apple juice and honey. Bring to the boil over a medium heat and simmer for 5 minutes. Remove and cool before passing through a food processor and then rubbing through a fine sieve to give a pipless liquid.

3 If you are making the granita without an ice cream maker, pour the fruit mixture into a freezer container and place in the freezer for 2–3 hours, or until a frozen slush is formed. Stir every 30 minutes to break up the ice crystals. Alternatively, assemble the ice cream maker, switch on and pour in the fruit liquid. Allow to freeze for 35–45 minutes, or follow the manufacturer's instructions, until a frozen slush is formed.

4 Spoon into chilled glasses or individual glass dishes and decorate with mint sprigs or extra berries.

Serving Analysis			
Energy (kcals)	85	Protein (grams)	1.3
Total fat (grams)	0.3	Carbohydrate (grams)	10.6
of which saturated fat (grams)	0.1	of which sugars (grams)	10.6
Fat/100 g product (grams)	**0.1**		

15 minutes, plus
2 hours' cooling

25–35 minutes

GI low

Aromatic Pears

The aromatic spices of the East add an exotic dimension to these pears, making them absolutely delicious. Try them either warm or chilled with a spoonful of low-fat natural yogurt.

Cook's Tip

If liked, replace the apple juice with red or white wine, though this can raise the GI rating.

SERVES 6

6 whole pears, ripe but firm with stalks intact

1 tbsp lemon juice

2 tbsp clear honey

4 whole star anise

2 whole cloves

1 cinnamon stick, bruised

4 green cardamon pods, lightly cracked

450 ml/16 fl oz clear unsweetened apple juice

8% fat fromage frais or Greek yogurt, to serve

1 Peel the pears, leaving the stalks intact, and place in a large bowl. Cover with cold water and the lemon juice.

2 Place the honey with the spices and the apple juice in a large heavy-based saucepan and bring to the boil. Reduce the heat and simmer for 10 minutes.

3 Drain the pears and add to the saucepan, standing the pears upright. Cover with a lid then simmer for 15–25 minutes, or until tender when pierced with a skewer. Remove from the heat and allow to cool in the syrup, turning the pears or spooning the syrup occasionally over. Serve with 8% fat fromage frais or Greek yogurt.

Serving Analysis			
Energy (kcals)	88	Protein (grams)	0.7
Total fat (grams)	0.2	Carbohydrate (grams)	22.1
of which saturated fat (grams)	0	of which sugars (grams)	22.1
Fat/100 g product (grams)	**0.1**		

Warm Tropical Fruits

This makes a refreshing summer dessert, perfect for eating alfresco. Served slightly warm, these fruits are a delicious end to a perfect day.

Cook's Tip

Passion fruit are ripe when they are wrinkly. Unripe fruits will take about 3–5 days to ripen. Leave at room temperature.

SERVES 4

1 ripe mango	2 ripe passion fruit
1 ripe pawpaw	1 tbsp clear honey
225 g/8 oz lychees	150 ml/5 fl oz water
1 kiwi fruit	half-fat crème fraîche or 8% fat fromage frais, to serve

1 Peel the mango then stand on a chopping board and, with a sharp knife, cut down the fruit as near to the stone as possible. Turn the fruit slightly after each cut. When the fruit has been removed, cut the flesh into small wedges or dice.

2 Cut the pawpaw in half, scoop out and discard the seeds, peel and cut into small wedges or dice.

3 Peel the lychees, make a small slit down each fruit and carefully remove the stone. Peel the kiwi and cut into small wedges. Reserve.

4 Cut the passion fruit in half and scoop out the flesh and seeds. Place in a heavy-based saucepan with the honey and the water. Place over a gentle heat, stirring occasionally, until the honey has dissolved. Bring to the boil and boil for 2 minutes. Reduce the heat to a simmer and heat very gently for 5 minutes. Remove from the heat and leave for 15 minutes, or until you are ready to heat the fruits.

5 Strain the juice if liked, return to the saucepan and discard the passion fruit seeds. Add all the prepared fruits. Simmer for 3–5 minutes, or until the fruits are warm. Serve with the half-fat crème fraîche or 8% fat fromage frais.

Serving Analysis			
Energy (kcals)	91	Protein (grams)	1.7
Total fat (grams)	0.2	Carbohydrate (grams)	21.7
of which saturated fat (grams)	0	of which sugars (grams)	17.5
Fat/100 g product (grams)	**0.1**		

Baked Peaches

Although quick and easy to prepare and cook, this provides a stunning and elegant dessert which will be enjoyed by all. Fresh peaches or nectarines, when in season, are best, but if unavailable use peach halves, canned in fruit juice.

SERVES 4

4 large fresh ripe peaches

25 g/1 oz dried apricots

25 g/1 oz blueberries

1 tbsp flaked almonds, toasted

2 tbsp medium sherry or orange juice

fresh mint sprigs or lemon balm sprigs, to decorate

8% fat fromage frais or frozen yogurt, to serve

1 Preheat the oven to 180°C/350°F/Gas Mark 4. Cut the peaches in half and remove the stones. Place in an ovenproof dish.

2 Finely chop the apricots and place in a bowl with the blueberries and stir. Use to fill the hollows left by the removal of the peach stones. Sprinkle with the almonds.

3 Pour over the sherry then bake in the oven for 10 minutes, or until heated through. Serve decorated with mint or lemon balm sprigs and 8% fat fromage frais or frozen yogurt.

Cook's Tip

If preferred, peel the peaches. To do this, make a small cross at the stalk end of each fruit. Place the peaches in a large bowl and pour boiling water over them. Leave for 2 minutes then lift one out and, when cool enough to handle, peel. Repeat with the other peaches.

Serving Analysis			
Energy (kcals)	68	Protein (grams)	1.9
Total fat (grams)	2.2	Carbohydrate (grams)	9.1
of which saturated fat (grams)	0.2	of which sugars (grams)	9
Fat/100 g product (grams)	**2.4**		

15 minutes, plus
2 hours' cooling

12–15 minutes

GI low

Fruit Fool

Fruit Fools can be served for both formal or informal occasions and provide an ideal finale to any meal.

SERVES 4

350 g/12 oz red plums, stoned

4 tbsp orange juice

2–3 tsp clear honey, or to taste

350 g/12 oz fresh strawberries, sliced
   if large

2–3 tsp gelatine

6 tbsp low-fat natural yogurt

TO DECORATE

extra fruit

fresh mint sprigs

1 If the plums are very ripe, peel then slice and place in a saucepan with 2 tablespoons of the orange juice and the honey. Bring to the boil, then reduce the heat, cover and simmer for 5–10 minutes, or until soft. Add half the strawberries and simmer for a further 5 minutes.

2 Remove and cool then blend in a food processor with the remaining strawberries to form a purée.

3 Place the remaining orange juice in a heatproof bowl, placed over a pan of gently simmering water. Sprinkle in the gelatine and stir frequently for about 3 minutes, or until the gelatine is dissolved. Cool then stir into the fruit purée. Leave until cold.

4 Add the yogurt to the cold purée and stir lightly to give a rippled effect. Spoon into glasses and chill until required. Serve with extra fruit or fresh mint sprigs.

Serving Analysis			
Energy (kcals)	117	Protein (grams)	6.5
Total fat (grams)	0.8	Carbohydrate (grams)	22.5
of which saturated fat (grams)	0.3	of which sugars (grams)	22.5
Fat/100 g product (grams)	**0.3**		

Raspberry Sponge

Now and again everyone needs a comfort hit and this is just the thing: light fluffy sponge, topped with ripe, mouthwatering raspberries and some half-fat fromage frais. For a real treat, add a sprinkling of grated chocolate.

Cook's Tip

The egg and sugar mixture is thick enough if it leaves a trail when the whisk is dragged lightly over the surface.

SERVES 8

2 eggs

55 g/2 oz caster sugar

1 tsp vanilla essence

85 g/3 oz plain flour

1 tbsp cooled boiled water

150 ml/5 fl oz 8% fromage frais

350 g/12 oz fresh raspberries

1 tbsp grated plain dark chocolate (optional)

1 Preheat the oven to 220°C/425°F/Gas Mark 7. Lightly oil and line a 25 x 20-cm/ 10 x 8-inch baking tin with non-stick baking paper. Place the eggs, sugar and vanilla essence over a saucepan of gently simmering water and whisk for 5–8 minutes, or until really thick and creamy.

2 Remove from the heat and continue to whisk until cool. Sift the flour into the mixture and stir in lightly, adding the water. Spoon into the prepared tin and tap the tin lightly on the work surface to remove the air bubbles.

3 Bake in the preheated oven for 10–12 minutes, or until well risen and the top springs back when touched lightly with a clean finger. Remove and cool.

4 When you are ready to serve, discard the lining paper and cut the cake into 8 squares. Top each square with fromage frais and some raspberries. Sprinkle with a little grated chocolate if liked, and serve.

Serving Analysis

Energy (kcals)	115	Protein (grams)	4.9
Total fat (grams)	2.4	Carbohydrate (grams)	19.5
of which saturated fat (grams)	0.8	of which sugars (grams)	11.4
Fat/100 g product (grams)	2.5		

Index